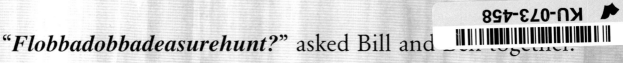
"*Flobbadobbadeasurehunt?*" asked Bill and Ben together.
"A treasure hunt is when you look around for
something interesting and bring it back," giggled Weed.

"The Man has lost
something shiny that
ticks, and some buttons,"
she added. "Why don't
you look for them?"

Bill and Ben zipped off to start hunting round and round and up and down all the paths in the garden.

Bill and Ben couldn't see any treasure in next door's garden.
"Oh, flubbalub!" huffed Ben. He was very disappointed.

Bill and Ben looked everywhere for the something shiny that ticked, and the lost buttons.

Bill and Ben thought they heard ticking, but it was just the sound of their boots on the path.

Bill asked Slowcoach if he'd seen any treasure. "No, I can't say I have," he replied.

"*Flobbadeasure?*" Bill asked Scamper. "No," she replied. "I haven't seen any treasure at all, I'm afraid."

The flowerpot men asked Boo
if he'd spotted any treasure.
"No, just slugs," replied Boo.

"Flobbadeasure?" Bill asked Rose.

"*I'm* the only treasure you'll find in *this* garden," she replied.

Ben found a shiny fork and trowel in the
vegetable patch. He bent down
to see if they ticked.